IT'S EASY TO PLAY

TOP 50 HITS

Wise Publications
London/New York/Paris/Sydney/Copenhagen/Madrid/Tokyo

Exclusive Distributors:

Music Sales Limited
8/9 Frith Street,
London W1V 5TZ, England.

Music Sales Pty Limited
120 Rothschild Avenue,
Rosebery, NSW 2018,
Australia.

Order No. AM958650
ISBN 0-7119-8024-1
This book © Copyright 2000 by Wise Publications

Book design by Chloë Alexander
Cover photographs courtesy of All Action/LFI/Retna

Music Sales' complete catalogue describes thousands of titles and is available in
full colour sections by subject, direct from Music Sales Limited. Please state your
areas of interest and send a cheque/postal order for £1.50 for postage to:
Music Sales Limited, Newmarket Road, Bury St. Edmunds, Suffolk IP33 3YB.

www.musicsales.com

Your Guarantee of Quality
As publishers, we strive to produce every book to the highest commercial
standards. This book has been carefully designed to minimise awkward page
turns and to make playing from it a real pleasure. Particular care has been given
to specifying acid-free, neutral-sized paper made from pulps which have not
been elemental chlorine bleached. This pulp is from farmed sustainable forests
and was produced with special regard for the environment. Throughout, the
printing and binding have been planned to ensure a sturdy, attractive
publication which should give years of enjoyment. If your copy fails to meet our
high standards, please inform us and we will gladly replace it.

Printed in the United Kingdom by
Caligraving Limited, Thetford, Norfolk.

BENNIE AND THE JETS ELTON JOHN **4**

BIG SPENDER SHIRLEY BASSEY **7**

BLUE BAYOU ROY ORBISON **10**

CAN'T HELP FALLING IN LOVE ELVIS PRESLEY **14**

DANCING QUEEN ABBA **16**

DON'T LOOK BACK IN ANGER OASIS **20**

DON'T STAND SO CLOSE TO ME THE POLICE **24**

EIGHT DAYS A WEEK THE BEATLES **28**

FATHER AND SON BOYZONE **30**

FROM A DISTANCE BETTE MIDLER **34**

GET BACK THE BEATLES **39**

HOLDING BACK THE YEARS SIMPLY RED **40**

I WILL ALWAYS LOVE YOU WHITNEY HOUSTON **44**

LADY MADONNA THE BEATLES **46**

MAKE IT EASY ON YOURSELF THE WALKER BROTHERS **49**

MR TAMBOURINE MAN THE BYRDS **52**

MRS ROBINSON SIMON & GARFUNKEL **54**

MULL OF KINTYRE WINGS **58**

ONE MORE NIGHT PHIL COLLINS **62**

PRIVATE DANCER TINA TURNER **65**

RETURN TO SENDER ELVIS PRESLEY **72**

RUNAWAY THE CORRS **68**

SHE ELVIS COSTELLO **75**

SO YOUNG THE CORRS **78**

SON OF A PREACHER MAN DUSTY SPRINGFIELD **82**

SWAY DEAN MARTIN **86**

TAKE MY BREATH AWAY BERLIN **88**

THE BOXER SIMON & GARFUNKEL **91**

THE UNIVERSAL BLUR **100**

THIS WHEEL'S ON FIRE JULIE DRISCOLL, BRIAN AUGER & THE TRINITY **96**

THREE LIONS '98 BADDIEL AND SKINNER AND THE LIGHTNING SEEDS **103**

2 BECOME 1 SPICE GIRLS **106**

VINCENT DON McCLEAN **109**

WATERLOO ABBA **114**

WILD WOOD PAUL WELLER **112**

WIND OF CHANGE THE SCORPIONS **117**

YOU ARE NOT ALONE MICHAEL JACKSON **120**

YOU GOTTA BE DES'REE **124**

BENNIE AND THE JETS

Words & Music by Elton John & Bernie Taupin

Moderately slow, in 2

Hey, kids, shake it loose to-geth-er; the spot-light's hit-ting some-thing that's been
Hey, kids, plug in-to the faith-less; may-be they're blind-ed but

known to change the wea-ther. We'll kill the fat-ted calf to-night,__ so stick a-
Ben-nie makes them age-less. We shall sur - vive; let us take our-selves a -

round. _____ You're gon - na hear e - lec - tric
long _____

mu - sic, sol - id walls of sound. Say,
streets to find who's right and who's wrong.

Can - dy and Ron - nie, have you seen them yet? Oo, but they're so spaced

out, ___ B - B - B - B - B - Ben - nie and the jets.

Oh, but they're weird ___ and they're won - der - ful, oh Ben - nie, she's real - ly keen; ___

5

BIG SPENDER

Words by Dorothy Fields
Music by Cy Coleman

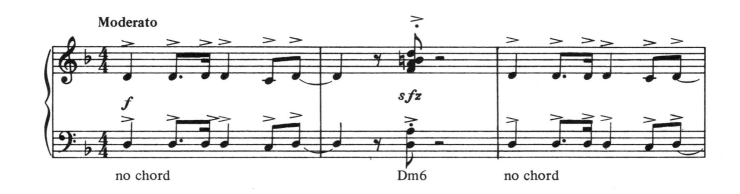

Moderato

no chord   Dm6   no chord

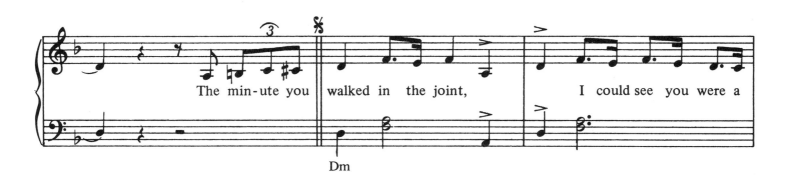

The min-ute you walked in the joint, I could see you were a

Dm

man of dis-tinc-tion, a real Big Spend-er. Good look-ing,

Bb   E7   A7

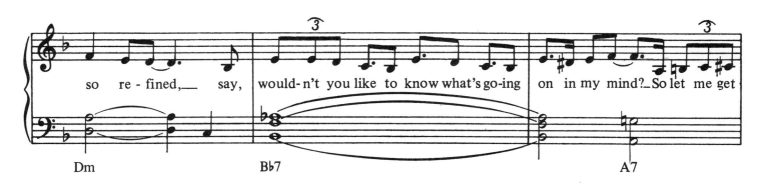

so re-fined, say, would-n't you like to know what's go-ing on in my mind?_ So let me get

Dm   Bb7   A7

right to the point, I don't pop my cork for ev-'ry guy I see.

Dm   Bb

To Coda ✛

Hey! Big Spend-er,   Spend

E7   Dm   no chord   Bb7

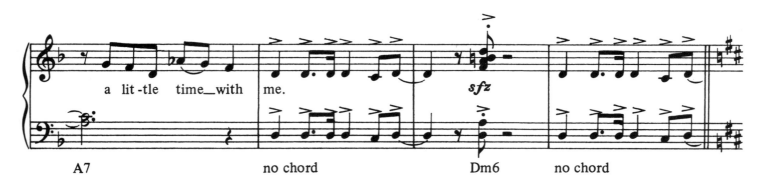

a lit-tle time___with me.   *sfz*

A7   no chord   Dm6   no chord

Would-n't you like to have fun, fun, fun? How's a-bout a few

D   F#m   D6

Em   G+   Em7

laughs, laughs?___   I can show you a   good time,___

Em   G+   Em7   Bb7

8

BLUE BAYOU

Words & Music by Roy Orbison & Joe Melson

Moderately

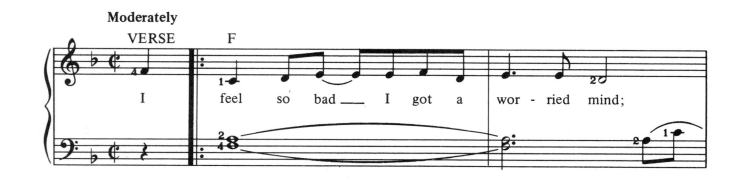

I feel so bad ___ I got a wor - ried mind;

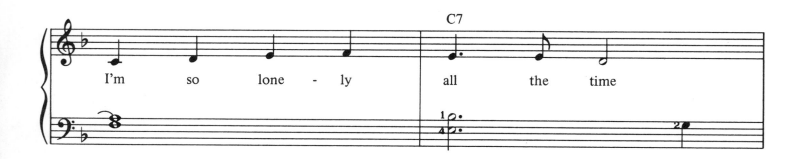

I'm so lone - ly all the time

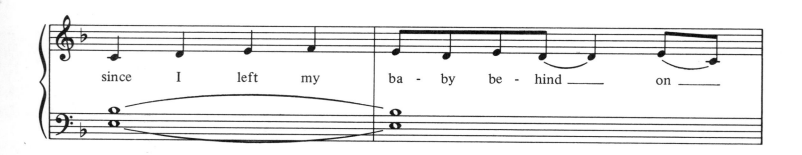

since I left my ba - by be - hind ___ on ___

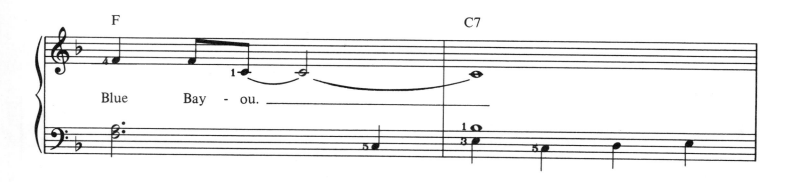

Blue Bay - ou. _____

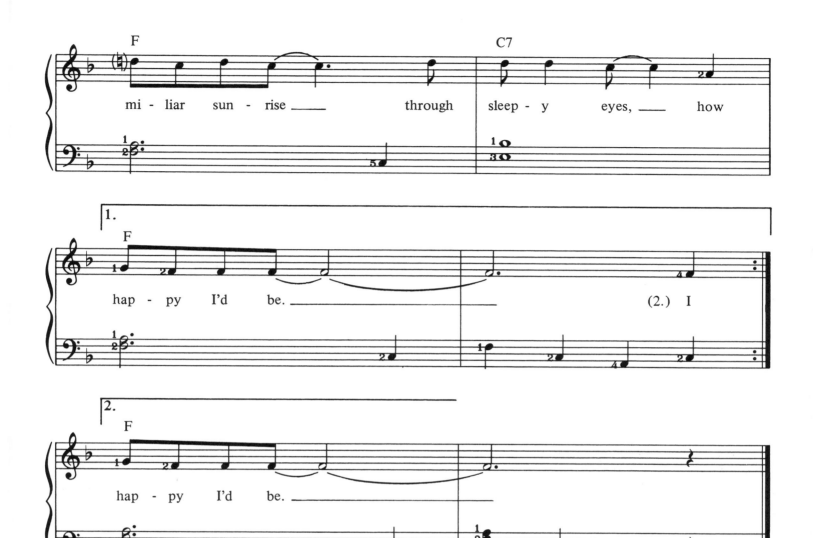

VERSE 2:
I feel so bad, I got a worried mind,
I'm so lonely all the time
Since I left my baby behind on Blue Bayou.
Saving nickles, saving dimes, working 'till the sun don't shine,
Looking forward to happier times on Blue Bayou.

CHORUS 2:
I'm going back someday, gonna stay on Blue Bayou;
Where my folks I'll find, all the time on Blue Bayou.
With that girl of mine by my side
Till the moon in the evening dies,
Oh, some sweet day, gonna take away this hurtin' inside.

CAN'T HELP FALLING IN LOVE

Words & Music by George Weiss, Hugo Peretti & Luigi Creatore

1. Wise men say only fools rush in, But I can't help fall-ing in love with you.
2. Shall I stay, would it be a sin, If I can't help fall-ing in love with you.

DANCING QUEEN

Words & Music by Benny Andersson, Björn Ulvaeus & Stig Anderson

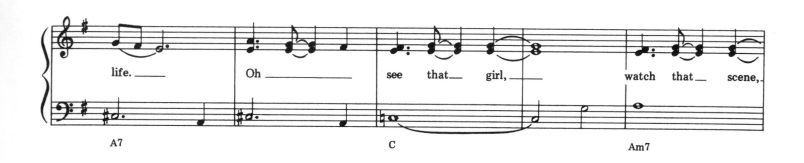

Fri - day night___ and the lights are low,___

C   G   C

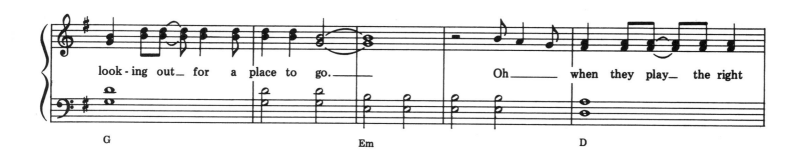

look - ing out___ for a place to go.___   Oh_____ when they play___ the right

G   Em   D

mu - sic,   get - ting in___ the swing,   You come to look for a king.___

G   D   G   D   Em

1. A - ny - bod - y could be that guy;
2. You're a tea - ser, you turn 'em on,___

D   Em   C

night is young___ and the mu - sic's   high.___
leave 'em burn - ing and then you're   gone.___

G   Em

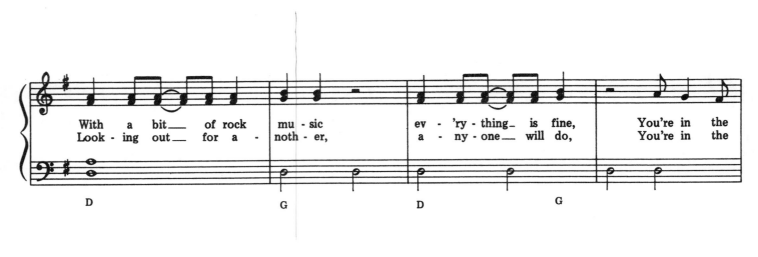

With a bit__ of rock mu - sic ev - 'ry - thing__ is fine, You're in the
Look - ing out__ for a - noth - er, a - ny - one__ will do, You're in the

D   G   D   G

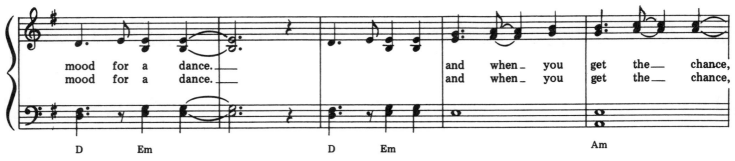

mood for a dance.__ and when__ you get the__ chance,
mood for a dance.__ and when__ you get the__ chance,

D   Em   D   Em   Am

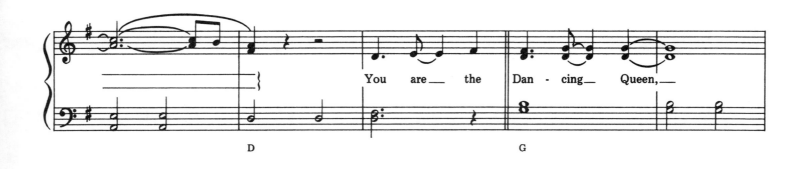

You are__ the Dan - cing__ Queen,__

D   G

Young and__ sweet,__ on - ly sev - en - teen.

C   G   D   G

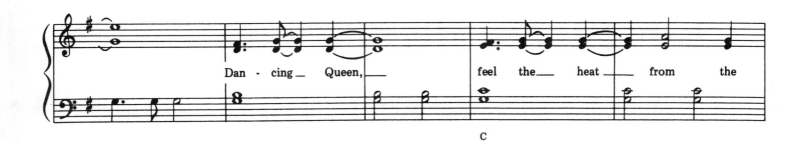

Dan - cing__ Queen,__ feel the__ heat__ from the

C

G   D   Em   G   D

tam - bou - rine. _____ You can dance,

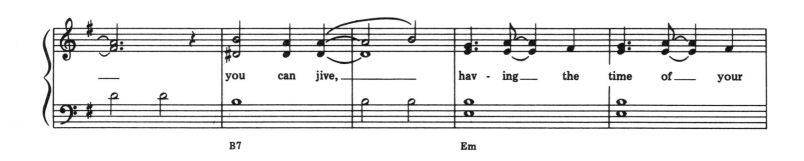

B7   Em

you can jive, _____ hav - ing _____ the time of _____ your

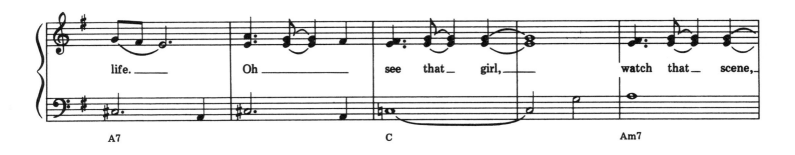

A7   C   Am7

life. _____ Oh _____ see that _ girl, _____ watch that _ scene,

G   D7   C   G   D7

1

_ dig in the Dan - cing _ Queen. _____

Repeat and Fade

2

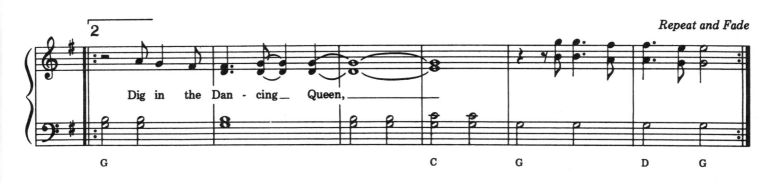

G   C   G   D   G

Dig in the Dan - cing _ Queen, _____

DON'T LOOK BACK IN ANGER

Words & Music by Noel Gallagher

1. Slip in-side the eye of your mind,
(Verse 2 see block lyric)

don't you know you might find ____ a bet-ter place to

play? ____ You said that you'd ne-ver been, ____

but all the things that you've seen_____ slow-ly fade a - way.

So I start a re-vo-lu-tion from my bed, 'cause you said the brains I had went to my

head. Step out-side, sum-mer-time's in bloom,

stand up be-side the fi-re-place, take that look from off your face,

you ain't ev-er gon-na burn my_____ heart___ out.

So Sal-ly can wait,——— she knows it's too late,———

—— as {we're / she's} walk — ing on by.——————— {her / my}

soul slides a - way.——— But don't look back in an - ger, I heard you

1. say.

2. *D.S. al Coda*
say.

CODA
say. So Sal-ly can wait,———

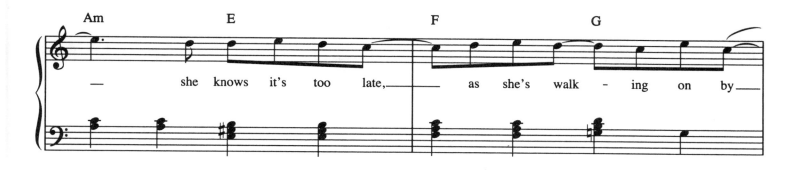

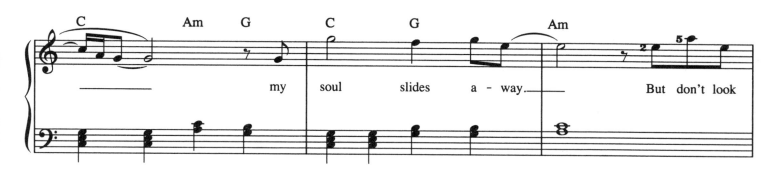

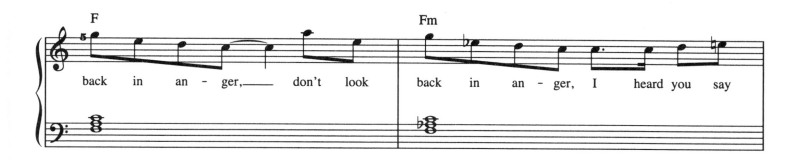

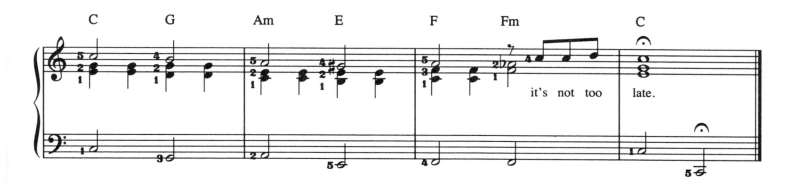

Verse 2:

Take me to the place where you go
Where nobody knows if it's night or day.
Please don't put your life in the hands
Of a rock 'n' roll band who'll throw it all away.

I'm gonna start a revolution from my head,
'Cause you said the brains I had went to my head.
Step outside, the summertime's in bloom,
Stand up beside the fireplace, take that look from off your face,
'Cause you ain't never gonna burn my heart out.

DON'T STAND SO CLOSE TO ME

Words & Music by Sting

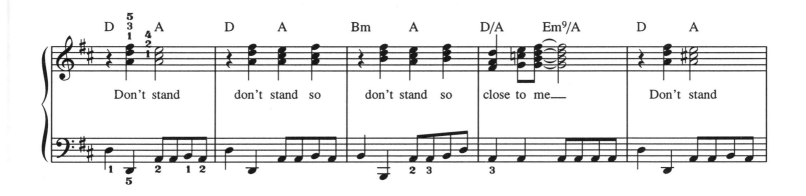

Don't stand   don't stand so   don't stand so   close to me___   Don't stand

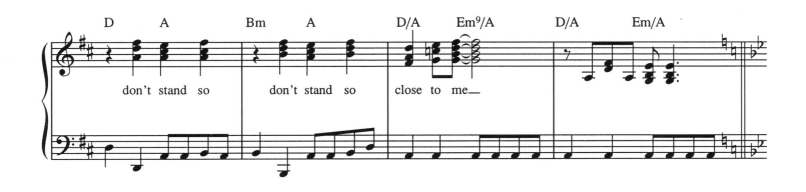

don't stand so   don't stand so   close to me___

𝄋 = Instrumental

Her   friends are___   so   jea - lous   you   know how   bad   girls   get___
Loose   talk in___   the   class-room   to   hurt they   try   and___   try

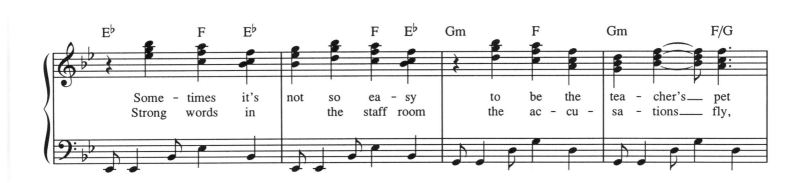

Some - times   it's   not   so   ea - sy   to   be   the   tea - cher's___   pet
Strong   words   in   the   staff room   the   ac - cu -   sa - tions___   fly,

Temp - ta - tion / frus - tra - tion / so bad it / makes him___ cry
It's no use / he sees her / he starts to / shake and___ cough

To Coda ⊕

wet bus stop / she's wait - ing / his car is / warm and___ dry.
Just like the / old man in / that book by / Na - ba - kov.

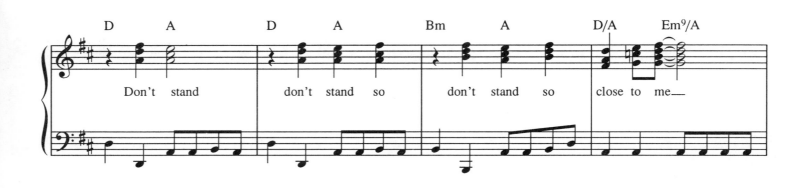

Don't stand / don't stand so / don't stand so / close to me___

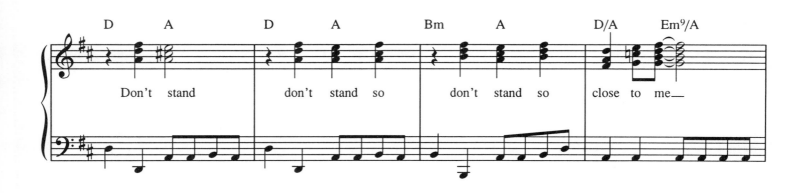

Don't stand / don't stand so / don't stand so / close to me___

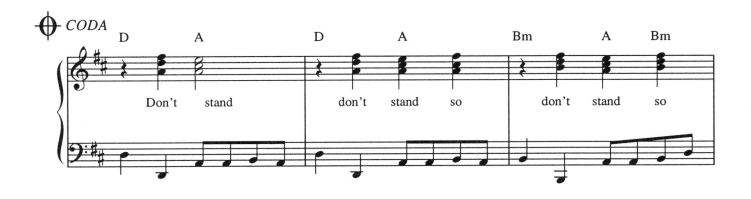

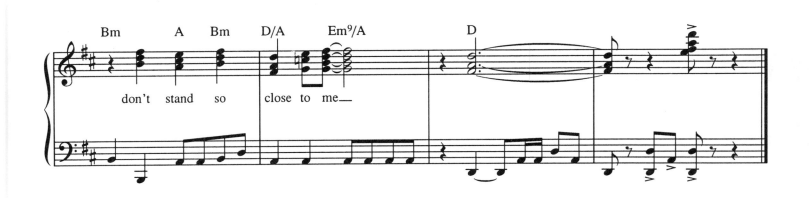

EIGHT DAYS A WEEK

Words & Music by John Lennon & Paul McCartney

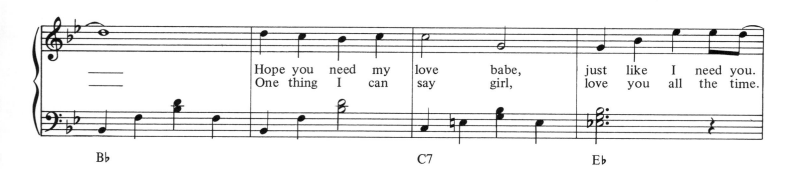

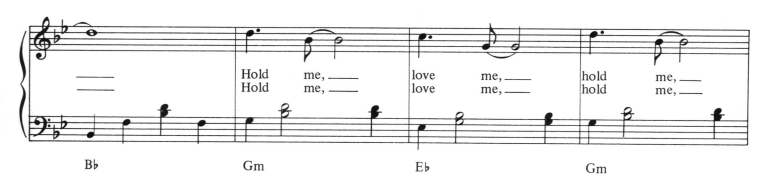

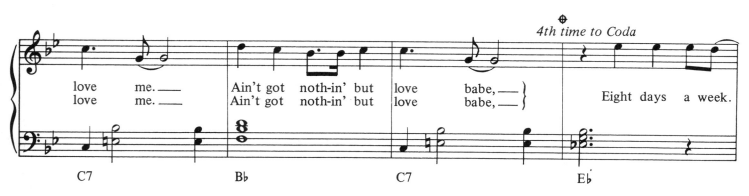

29

FATHER AND SON

Words & Music by Cat Stevens

1. It's not time to make a change; just re- lax, take it ea- sy. You're still
(Verse 2 see block lyric)

young, that's your fault; there's so much you have to know.— Find a girl,—

— set- tle down; if you want,— you can mar- ry. Look at

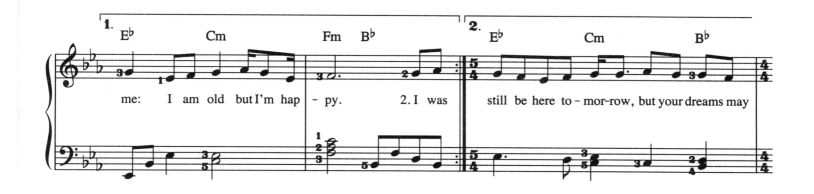

me: I am old but I'm hap - py. 2. I was

still be here to - mor-row, but your dreams may

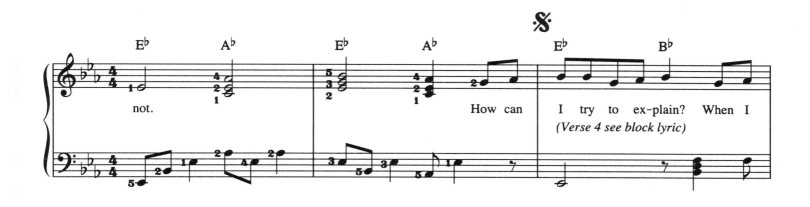

not.

How can I try to ex-plain? When I
(Verse 4 see block lyric)

do he turns a - way a - gain. Well, it's

al - ways been the same, same old

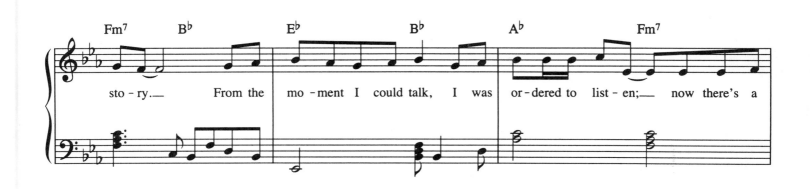

sto - ry.___ From the mo - ment I could talk, I was

or - dered to list - en;___ now there's a

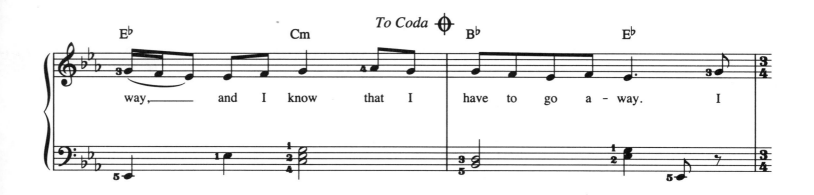

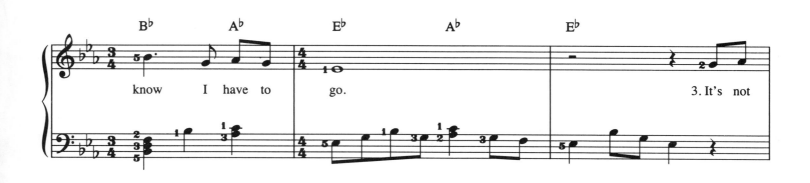

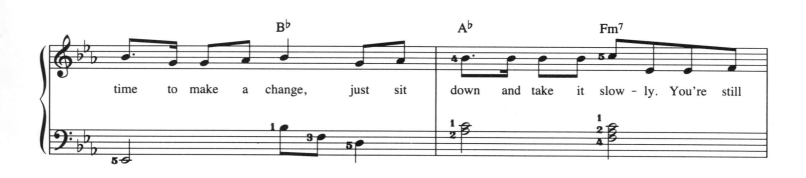

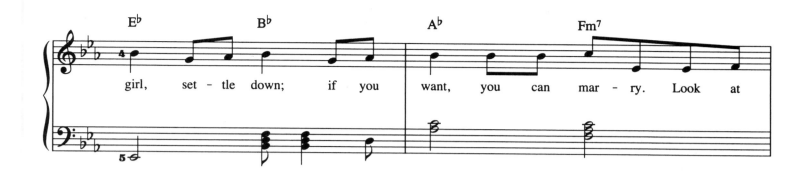

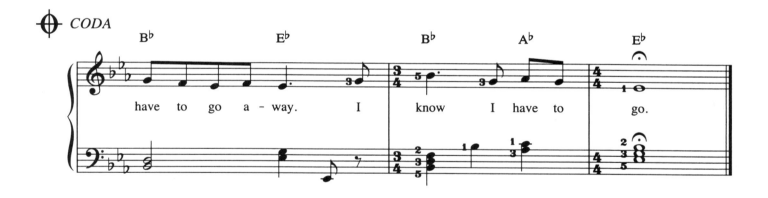

Verse 2:

I was once like you are now;
And I know that it's not easy
To be calm when you've found something going on.
But take your time, think a lot;
Think of everything you've got.
For you will still be here tomorrow,
But your dreams may not.

Verse 4:

All the times that I've cried,
Keeping all the things I knew inside;
And it's hard, but it's harder to ignore it.
If they were right I'd agree,
But it's them they know, not me;
Now there's a way, and I know
That I have to go away.
I know I have to go.

FROM A DISTANCE

Words & Music by Julie Gold

Moderately

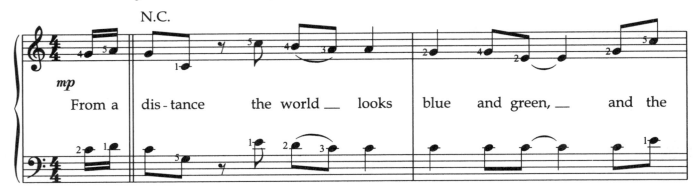

From a dis-tance the world ___ looks blue and green, ___ and the

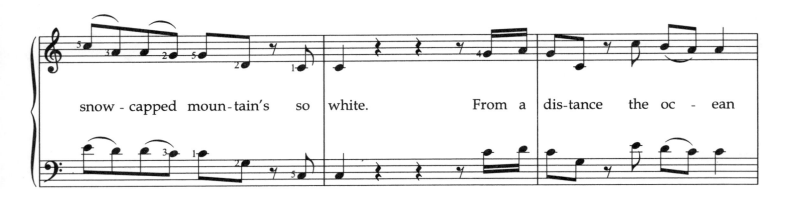

snow - capped moun-tain's so white. From a dis-tance the oc - ean

meets the stream, ___ and the ea - gle ___ takes ___ to flight. From a

dis-tance there ___ is har-mo-ny and it e - choes ___ through ___ the land.

GET BACK

Words & Music by John Lennon & Paul McCartney

Jo - jo was a man who thought he was a lon-er, but he knew it could-n't last.
Sweet Lo-ret-ta Mar-tin thought she was a wo-man, but she was an-oth-er man.

Jo - jo left his home in Tuc - son, Ar-i-zo-na for some Ca-li-for - nia grass.
All the girls a - round her say she's got it com-ing, But she gets it while she can.

Get back! Get back! Get back to where you once be-longed. Get back!

Get back! Get back to where you once be-longed.

HOLDING BACK THE YEARS

Words by Mick Hucknall
Music by Mick Hucknall & Neil Moss.
All Rights Reserved. International Copyright Secured.

Hold - ing back the years
Hold - ing back the years

think - ing of the fear I've had so long,
chance for me to es - cape from all I know,

when some - bo - dy hears
hold - ing back the tears

lis - ten to the fear that's gone.
there's noth - ing here has grown.

41

I WILL ALWAYS LOVE YOU

Words & Music by Dolly Parton

LADY MADONNA

Words & Music by John Lennon & Paul McCartney

47

Won – der how you man – aged to feed ____ the rest? ____
Lis – ten to the mu – sic playing in ____ your head. ____
Won – der how you man – age to make

ends meet. ____

MAKE IT EASY ON YOURSELF

Words by Hal David
Music by Burt Bacharach

Medium Slow

1. If you real- ly love him,
(Verse 2 see block lyric)

and there's no - thing

I can do;

don't try to spare my feel - ings,

just tell me that we're

through.

And make it ea-sy on your - self.

Make it ea - sy on your - self.

'Cos

Make it ea-sy on your-self. _____ 'Cos

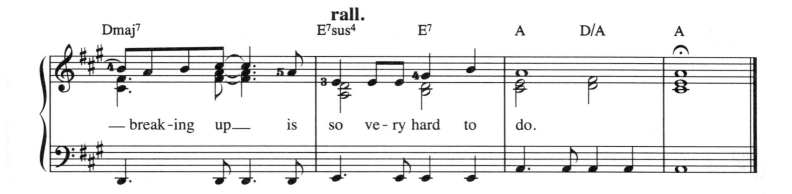

rall.

___ break-ing up ___ is so ve-ry hard to do.

2. And if the way I hold you
Can compare to his caress,
No words of consolation
Will make me miss you less.
My darling, if this is goodbye,
I just know I'm gonna cry;
So run to him before you start crying too.

And make it easy....

MR TAMBOURINE MAN

Words & Music by Bob Dylan

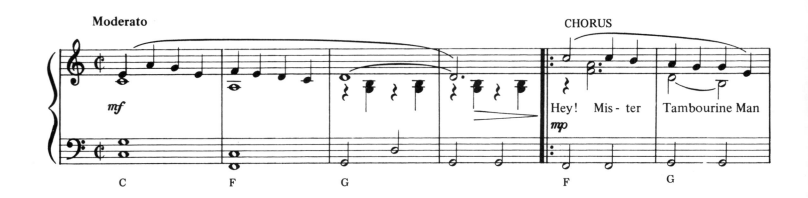

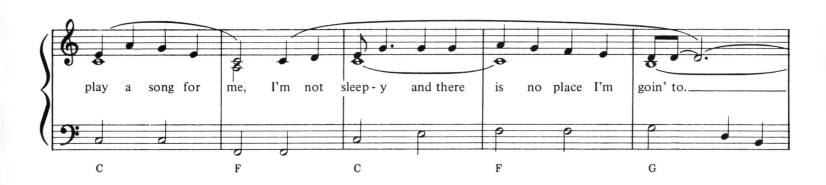

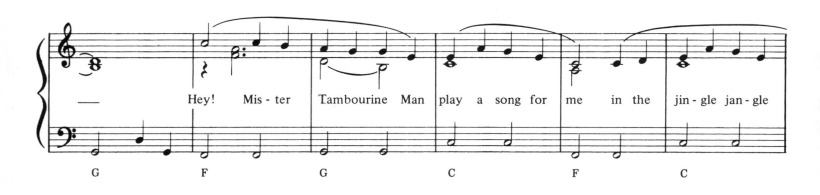

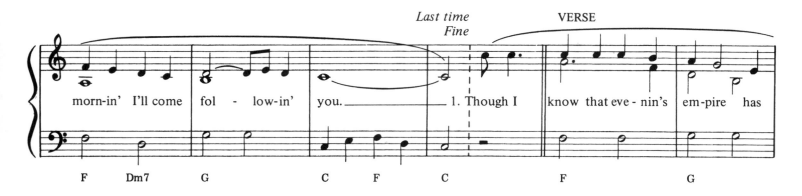

re-turned in-to sand, Va-nished from my hand, Left me blind-ly here to stand but still not

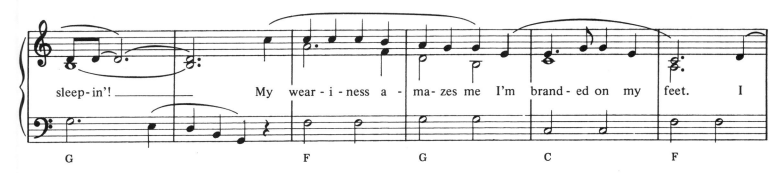

sleep-in'! _____ My wear-i-ness a - ma-zes me I'm brand-ed on my feet. I

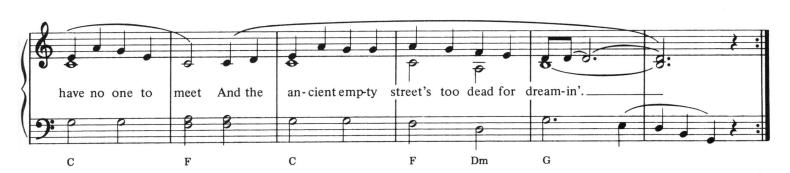

have no one to meet And the an-cient emp-ty street's too dead for dream-in'. _____

Chorus

2. Take me on a trip upon your magic swirlin' ship
   My senses have been stripped, my hands can't feel to grip
   My toes too numb to step, wait only for my boot heels
   To be wanderin'
   I'm ready to go anywhere, I'm ready for to fade
   Into my own parade, cast your dancin' spell my way
   I promise to go under it.
   Chorus

3. Though you might hear laughin' spinnin' swingin' madly across the sun
   It's not aimed at anyone, it's just escapin' on the run
   And but for the sky there are no fences facin'
   And if you hear vague traces of skippin' reels of rhyme
   To your tambourine in time, it's just a ragged clown behind
   I wouldn't pay it any mind, it's just a shadow you're
   Seein' that he's chasin'.
   Chorus

4. Then take me disappearin' through the smoke rings of my mind
   Down the foggy ruins of time, far past the frozen leaves
   The haunted, frightened trees out to the windy beach
   Far from the twisted reach of crazy sorrow
   Yes, to dance beneath the diamond sky with one hand wavin' free
   Silhouetted by the sea, circled by the circus sands
   With all memory and fate driven deep beneath the waves
   Let me forget about today until tomorrow.
   Chorus

MRS ROBINSON

Words & Music by Paul Simon

CHORUS

_ Mrs _ Rob - in - son, Je - sus loves you more _ than you will
_ Joe Di - mag - gi - o? A na - tion turns its lone - ly eyes to

C   Am   C   Am

know, _____ (Wo, wo, wo _____) God bless you
you, _____ (Woo, woo, woo _____) What's that you

F   Dm7   G7

please, Mrs _ Rob - in - son, Hea - ven holds a place _ for those who
say, Mrs _ Rob - in - son, "Jolt - in' Joe has left _ and gone a -

C   Am   C   Am

pray. _____ (Hey, hey, hey, _____ Hey, hey, hey.
way. _____ (Hey, hey, hey, _____ Hey, hey, hey.

F   Dm7   Dm

1   2

A   A

57

MULL OF KINTYRE

Words & Music by Paul McCartney & Denny Laine

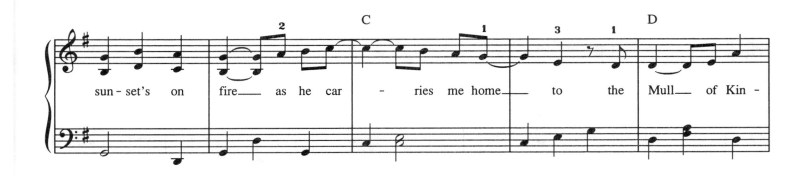

sun-set's on fire — as he car — ries me home — to the Mull — of Kin -

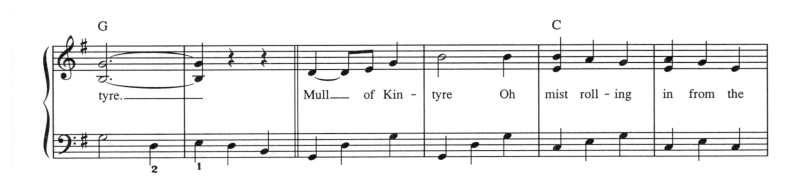

tyre. — Mull — of Kin - tyre Oh mist roll - ing in from the

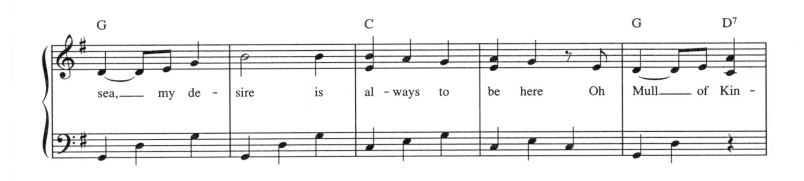

sea, — my de - sire is al - ways to be here Oh Mull — of Kin -

tyre. —

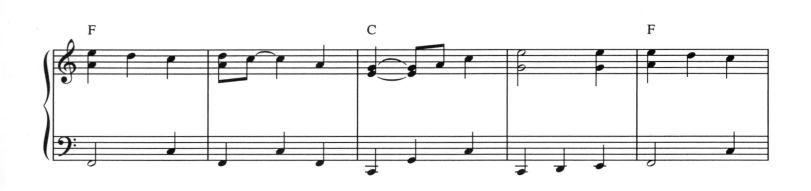

Sweep through_ the heath - er____ like deer in the glen Car - ry me

back to the days I knew then. Nights when we sang like a

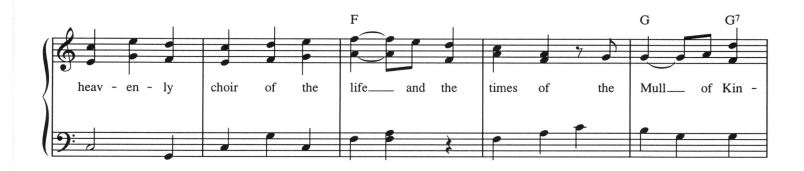

heav - en - ly   choir   of   the   life___ and   the   times   of   the   Mull___ of   Kin -

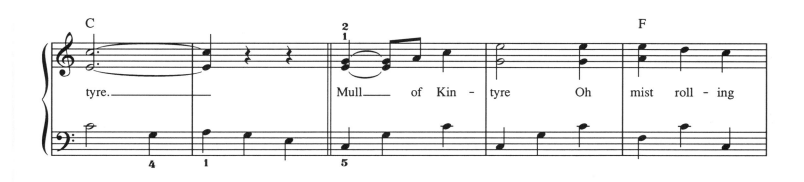

tyre._____   Mull___ of   Kin - tyre   Oh   mist   roll - ing

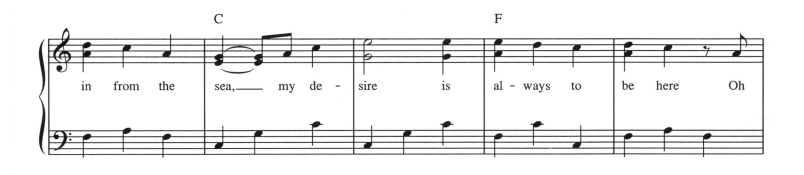

in   from   the   sea,___ my   de - sire   is   al - ways   to   be   here   Oh

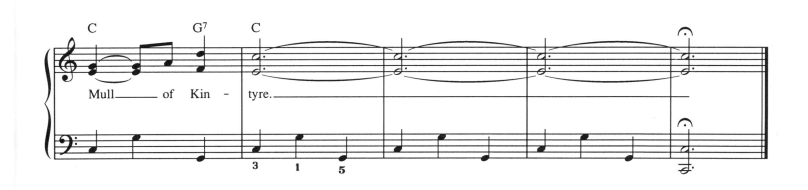

Mull___ of   Kin - tyre._____

ONE MORE NIGHT

Words & Music by Phil Collins

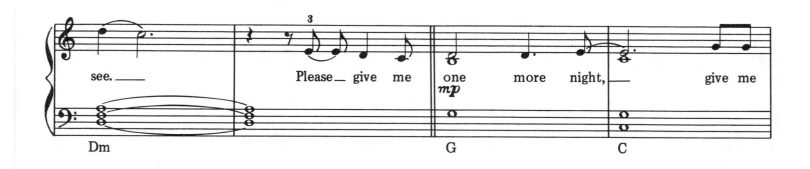

see. ____ Please ____ give me one more night, ____ give me

Dm   G   C

one more night, ____ one more night, ____ 'cause I can't wait fore - ver.

G   C   G   C   Dm

Give me just one more night, ____ oh just one more night, ____ oh, ____

G   G   C   G   C

one more night, ____ 'cause I can't wait for - ever.   Like a ri-

G   C   Dm   G   Am7

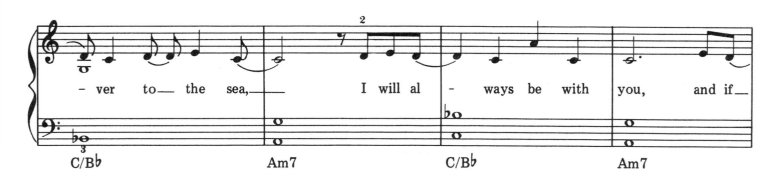

- ver to ____ the sea, ____ I will al - ways be with you, and if

C/B♭   Am7   C/B♭   Am7

you sail a - way,   I will fo - llow you.   Give me

C/B♭   Am7   B♭/C

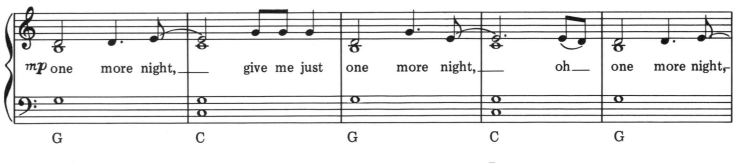

mp one   more night,   give me just one more night,   oh   one more night,

G   C   G   C   G

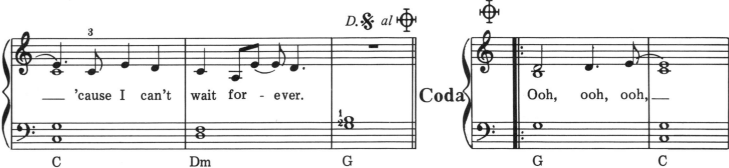

D. %: al ⊕

'cause I can't wait for - ever.   **Coda**   Ooh,   ooh,   ooh,

C   Dm   G   G   C

ooh,   ooh,   ooh,   ooh,   ooh,   ooh,   ooh,   ooh,   ooh.

G   C   G   C   Dm7   Am/D   G

2. I've been sitting here so long wasting time,
   Just staring at the phone.
   And I was wondering should I call you,
   Then I thought maybe you're not alone.
   Please give me one more night etc.

3. I know there'll never be a time you'll ever feel the same.
   And I know it's only right.
   But if you'll change your mind,
   You know that I'll be here,
   And maybe we both can learn.
   Give me just one more night etc.

PRIVATE DANCER

Words & Music by Mark Knopfler

66

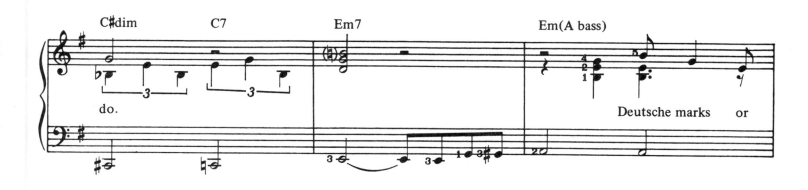

do.

Deutsche marks or

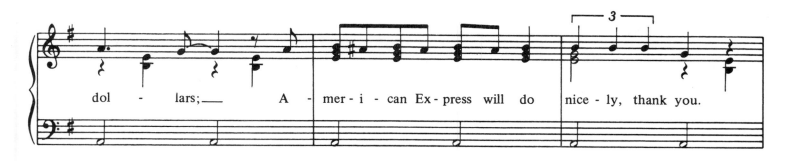

dol - lars;___ A - mer - i - can Ex - press will do nice - ly, thank you.

Let me loos - en up your col - lar,_____ tell me,

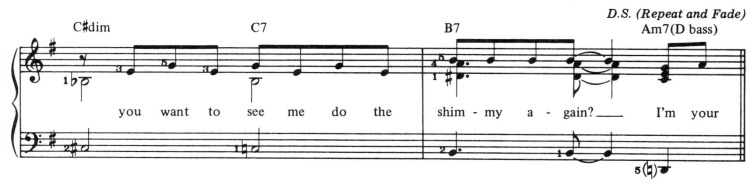

D.S. (Repeat and Fade)

you want to see me do the shim - my a - gain?___ I'm your

VERSE 2:
You don't think of them as human.
You don't think of them at all.
You keep your mind on the money,
Keeping your eyes on the wall.

(To Chorus:)

VERSE 3:
I want to make a million dollars.
I want to live out by the sea.
Have a husband and some children;
Yeah, I guess I want a family.

RUNAWAY

Words & Music by Andrea Corr, Caroline Corr, Sharon Corr & Jim Corr

you.

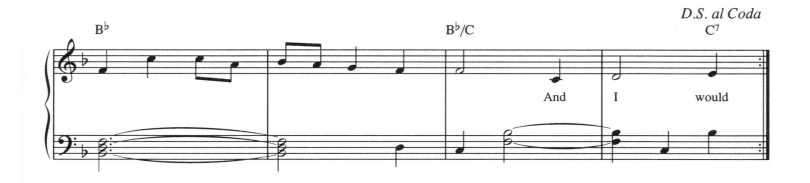

D.S. al Coda

B♭   B♭/C   C⁷

And   I   would

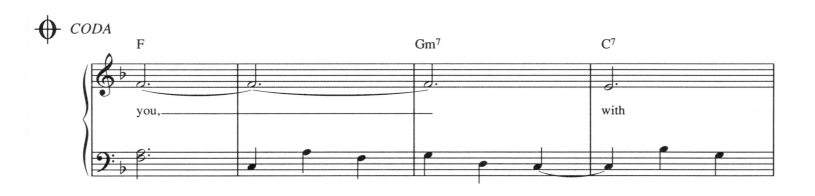

CODA

F   Gm⁷   C⁷

you,   with

F   Gm⁷   F

you.

RETURN TO SENDER

Words & Music by Otis Blackwell & Winfield Scott

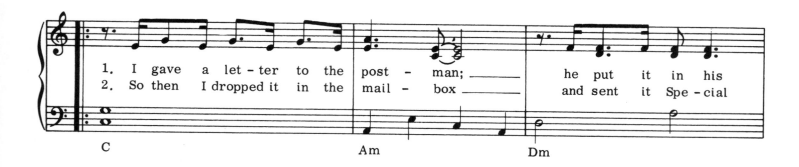

SHE

Words by Herbert Kretzmer
Music by Charles Aznavour

Moderately slow

1. She___ may be the face I can't for-get,___ a trace of plea-sure or re-

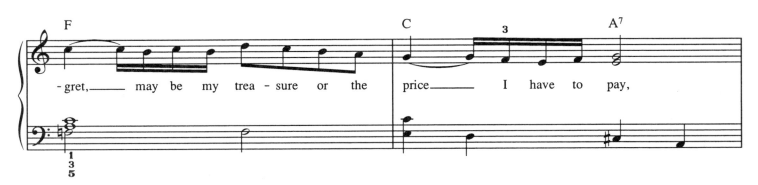

-gret,___ may be my trea-sure or the price___ I have to pay,

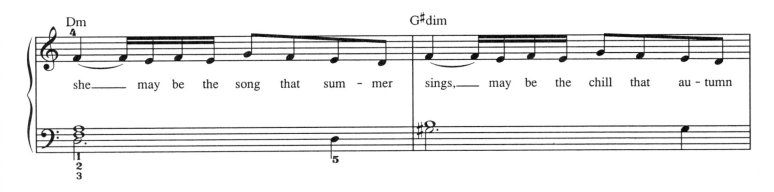

she___ may be the song that sum-mer sings,___ may be the chill that au-tumn

brings,__may be a hun-dred diff-'rent things__ with-in the mea-sure of a day.

2. She___ may be the beau-ty or the beast,___ may be the fa-mine or the
(Verse 3 instr. Verse 4 see block lyric)

feast,___ may turn each day in-to a hea - ven or___ hell.

She___ may be the mir – ror of my dreams___ a smile re -flec - ted in a

stream,__she may not be what she may seem, in - side her shell.

shell.

3° to Coda

She___ who al-ways seems so hap-py in a crowd,___ whose eyes can be so pri - vate and so

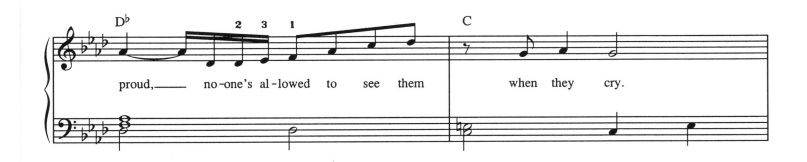

proud,____ no-one's al-lowed to see them when they cry.

She__ may be the love that can-not hope to last,__ may come to me from sha-dows of the

D.S. al Coda

past_____ that I'll re-mem-ber till the day I die.

CODA

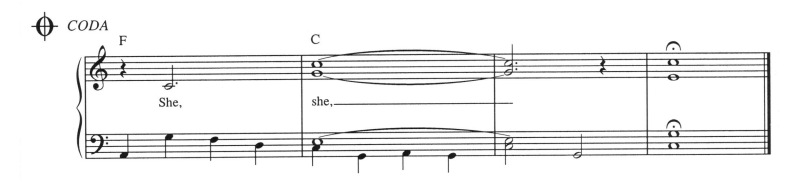

She, she,____

Verse 4:

She may be the reason I survive
The why and wherefore I'm alive
The one I'll care for through the rough and ready years.
Me, I'll take her laughter and her tears
And make them all my souvenirs
For where she goes I've got to be
The meaning of my life is she, she, she.

SO YOUNG

Words & Music by Andrea Corr, Caroline Corr, Sharon Corr & Jim Corr

CODA

We are so / Yeah yeah yeah yeah yeah. / young,

yeah, / We are so / Yeah yeah / young,

yeah yeah yeah. / We are so / young.

Verse 2:

We are chasing the moon
Just running wild and free,
We are following through
Every dream and every need.

'Cause we are so young now *etc.*

SON OF A PREACHER MAN

Words & Music by John Hurley & Ronnie Wilkins

on - ly boy who could ev - er reach me was the son of a preach - er man. The

on - ly one who could ev - er move me was the son of a preach - er man. The

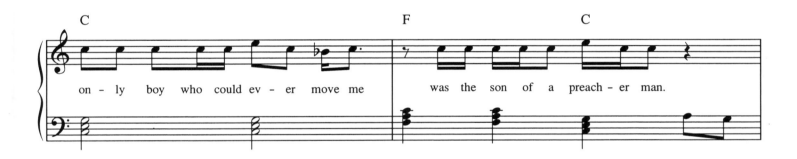

on - ly boy who could ev - er move me was the son of a preach - er man.

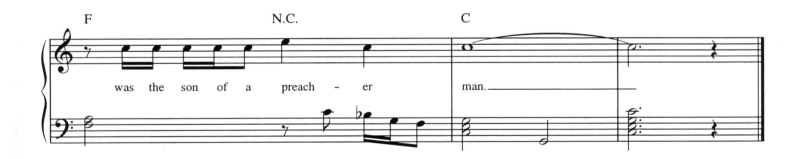

was the son of a preach - er man._____

Verse 2:

Being good isn't always easy
No matter how hard I try.
When he started sweet talking to me,
He'd come and tell me everything is all right,
He'd kiss and tell me everything is all right,
Can't get away again tonight.

SWAY

Words by Norman Gimbel
Music by Pablo Beltran Ruiz

Moderato

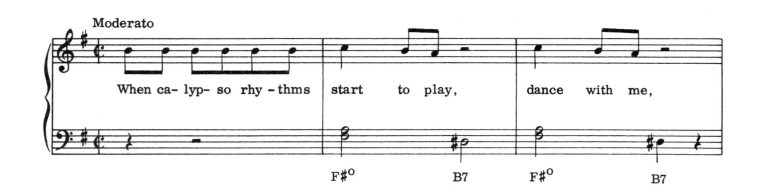

When ca- lyp- so rhy -thms start to play, dance with me,

F#⁰   B7   F#⁰   B7

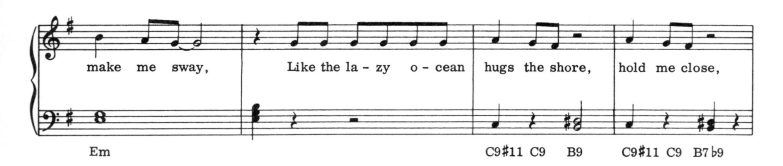

make me sway, Like the la - zy o - cean hugs the shore, hold me close,

Em   C9#11 C9   B9   C9#11 C9 B7♭9

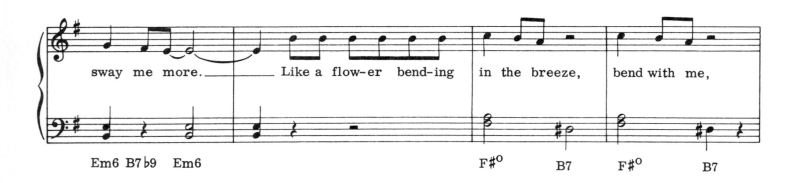

sway me more.___ Like a flow-er bend-ing in the breeze, bend with me,

Em6 B7♭9 Em6   F#⁰   B7   F#⁰   B7

sway with ease, When we dance you have a way with me, stay with me,

Em   C9#11 C9   B9   C9#11 C9 B7♭9

TAKE MY BREATH AWAY

Words by Tom Whitlock
Music by Giorgio Moroder

Moderately slow

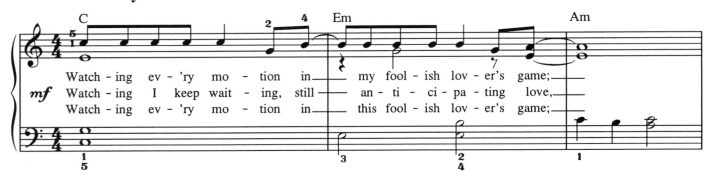

Watch - ing ev - 'ry mo - tion in my fool - ish lov - er's game;
Watch - ing I keep wait - ing, still an - ti - ci - pa - ting love,
Watch - ing ev - 'ry mo - tion in this fool - ish lov - er's game;

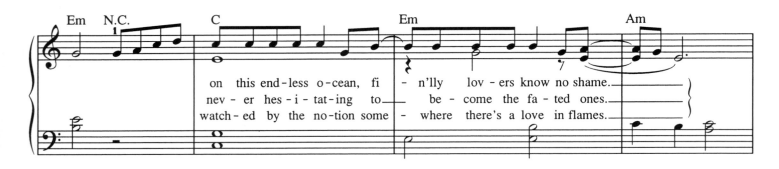

on this end - less o - cean, fi - n'lly lov - ers know no shame.
nev - er hes - i - tat - ing to be - come the fa - ted ones.
watch - ed by the no - tion some - where there's a love in flames.

Turn - ing and re - turn - ing to some se - cret place to hide;

watch - ing in slow mo - tion as

THE BOXER

Words & Music by Paul Simon

THE BOXER

Words & Music by Paul Simon

left my home and my fam - i - ly,___ I was no more than a boy, in the

com - pa - ny ___ of stran - gers, in the qui - et of a rail - way sta - tion

run - ning scared.___ Lay - ing low, seek - ing

out the poor - er quar - ters where the rag - ged peo - ple go, Look-ing

for the pla - ces on - ly they would know. Lie - la

92

THIS WHEEL'S ON FIRE

Words by Bob Dylan
Music by Rick Danko

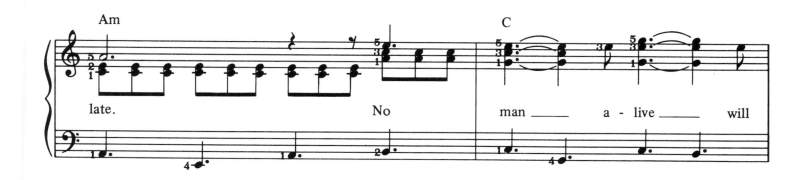

late.   No   man _____ a - live _____ will

come   to   you   with   an - oth - er _____ tale ___ to   tell,

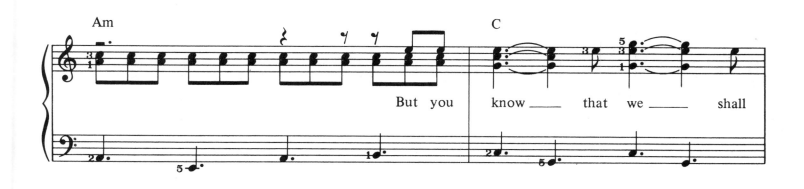

But   you   know _____ that   we _____ shall

meet   a - gain _____ if   your   mem - 'ry _____ serves   you

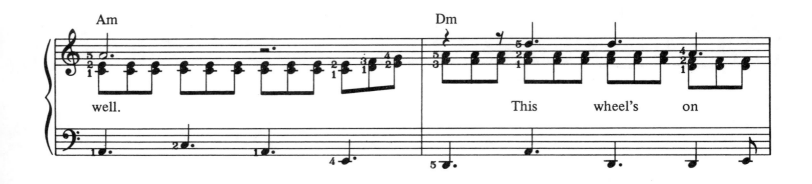

well.

This wheel's on

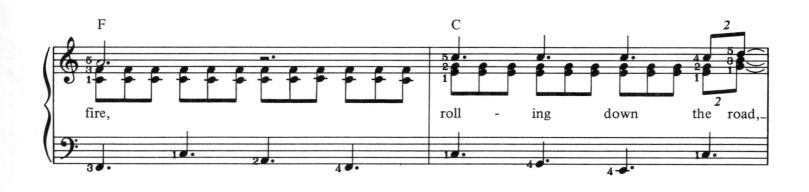

fire,

roll - ing down the road,

Best

no - ti - fy my

next of kin,

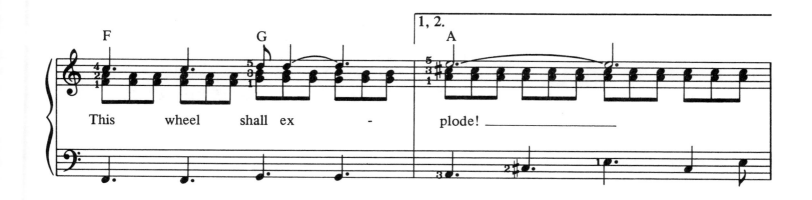

This wheel shall ex - plode! _____

(2.) If your - plode! _____

2. If your mem'ry serves you well,
   I was goin' to confiscate your lace,
   And wrap it up in a sailors knot
   And hide it in your case.
   If I knew for sure that it was yours
   But it was oh so hard to tell.
   But you knew that we would meet again,
   If your mem'ry serves you well.
   This wheel's on fire . . . . etc.

3. If your mem'ry serves you well,
   You'll remember you're the one that called on me
   To call on them to get you your favours done.
   And after ev'ry plan had failed
   And there was nothing more to tell,
   You knew that we would meet again,
   If your mem'ry served you well.
   This wheel's on fire . . . . etc.

THE UNIVERSAL

Words & Music by Damon Albarn, Graham Coxon, Alex James & Dave Rowntree

real - ly real - ly real - ly could hap - pen, yes, it real - ly real - ly real - ly could hap-

pen, when the days____ they seem to fall through you, well just let them go.____

1. 2. No

2. Well it

real - ly real - ly real - ly could hap - pen, yes, it real - ly real - ly real - ly could hap-

pen,   when the days   they seem to fall through you, well   just   let them   go.

Just   let   them   go.

Verse 2:

No one here is alone,
Satellites in every home,
The universal's here,
Here for everyone.

Every paper that you read
Says tomorrow's your lucky day,
Well, here's your lucky day.

THREE LIONS '98

Words by David Baddiel & Frank Skinner
Music by Ian Broudie

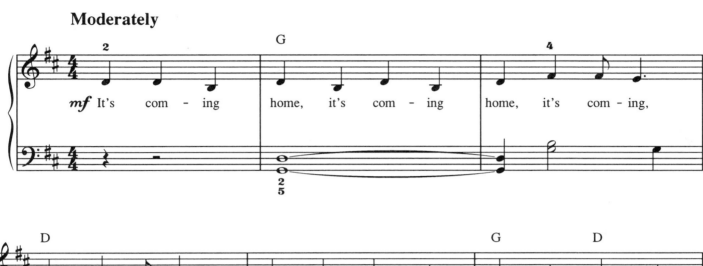

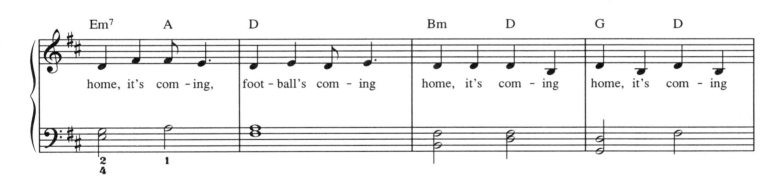

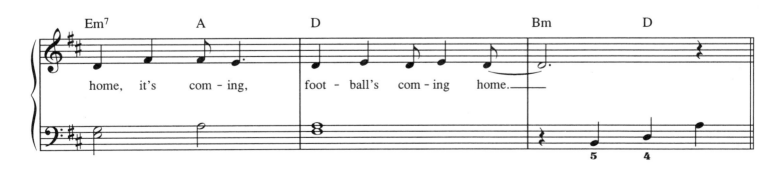

2 BECOME 1

Words & Music by Victoria Aadams, Melanie Brown, Emma Bunton,
Melanie Chisholm, Geri Halliwell, Matt Rowe & Richard Stannard

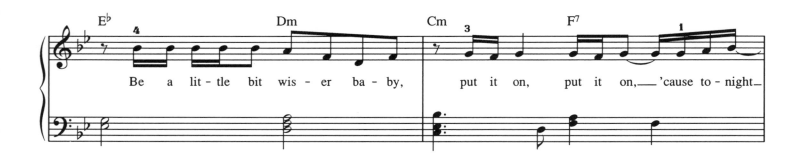

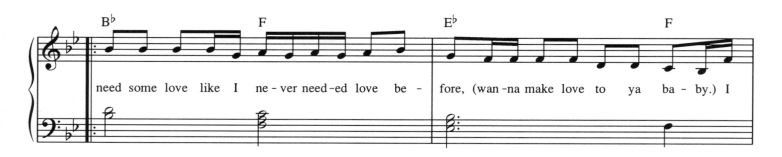

Verse 2:

Silly games that you were playing, empty words we both were saying,
Let's work it out boy, let's work it out boy.
Any deal that we endeavour, boys and girls feel good together,
Take it or leave it, take it or leave it.
Are you as good as I remember baby, get it on, get it on,
'Cause tonight is the night when two become one.

I need some love like I never needed love before, (wanna make love to ya baby.)
I had a little love, now I'm back for more, (wanna make love to ya baby.)
Set your spirit free, it's the only way to be.

VINCENT

Words & Music by Don McLean

Starry, Starry Night (Vincent)

G | C | G | Am
land._____ | | Now I un-der- stand
hand._____ | | Now I un-der- stand
snow._____ | | Now I think I know

D7 | G | Em | G
what you tried to say to me, | how you suf-fered for your

Am7 | D7 | Em | *To Coda*
sa-ni-ty, | how you tried to set them | free. They would not lis-ten, 1,2. they did
| | | 3. they're not

A7 | Am7 | D7 | **1.** G
not know how,___ | per-haps they'll lis-ten | now._____

Em | G | **2.** G | Am7
___ Star-ry, star-ry | now. For they could not | love you,

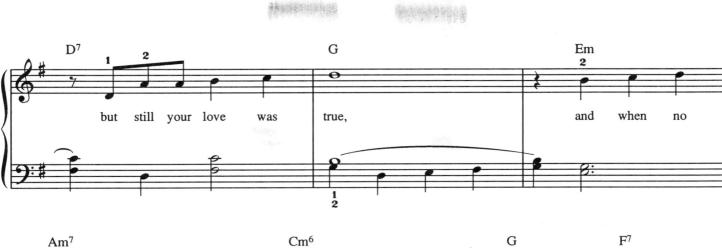

but still your love was true, and when no

hope was left in sight— on that star-ry, star-ry night, you took your life, as lov-ers of-ten

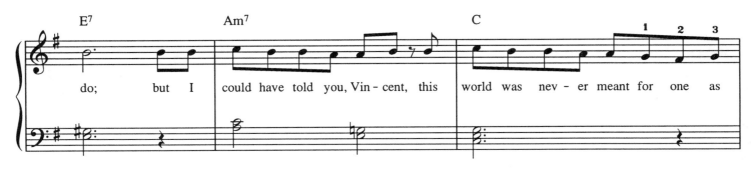

do; but I could have told you, Vin-cent, this world was nev-er meant for one as

D.S. al Coda

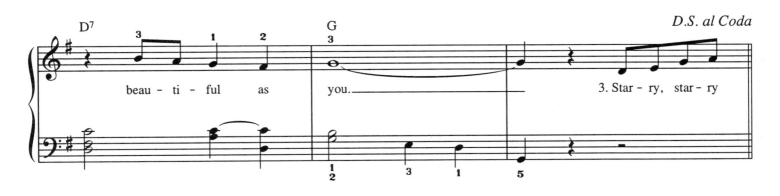

beau-ti-ful as you._____ 3. Star-ry, star-ry

⊕ CODA

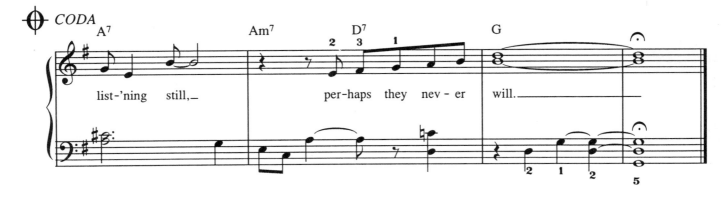

list-'ning still,— per-haps they nev-er will._____

WILD WOOD

Words & Music by Paul Weller

Verse 2:

Don't let them get you down,
Making you feel guilty about
Golden rain will bring you riches,
All the good things you deserve now.

Verse 3:

Climbing, forever trying,
Find your way out of the wild wild wood.
Now there's no justice,
You've only yourself that you can trust in.

Verse 4:

And I said high tide, mid-afternoon,
People fly by in the traffic's boom.
Knowing just where you're blowing,
Getting to where you should be going.

Verse 5:

Day by day your world fades away,
Waiting to feel all the dreams that say,
Golden rain will bring you riches,
All the good things you deserve now.

WATERLOO

Words & Music by Benny Andersson, Björn Ulvaeus & Stig Anderson

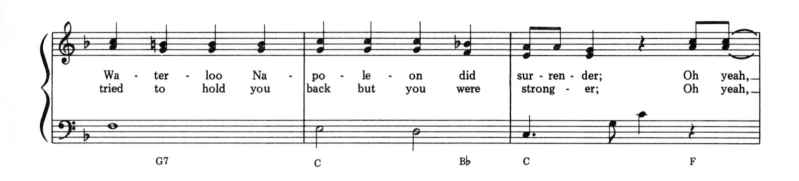

shelf   is   al - ways re - peat - ing it - self,_____
- fuse   I   feel like I win when I lose._____

G7   C

Wa - ter - loo,   I was de - feat - ed, you won the war.

F   C7   F   Bb

Wa - ter - loo,   pro - mise to love you for ev - er - more.

C   F   Bb   C

Wa - ter - loo,   Could - n't es - cape if I want - ed to.

F   C7   F   Bb

Wa - ter - loo,   Know - ing my fate is to be with you.   Wa, Wa, Wa, Wa,

C   F

116

WIND OF CHANGE

Words & Music by Klaus Meine

118

The wind of change blows straight in-to the face_ of time _ like a storm wind that will

ring the free-dom bell, _ for peace of mind,_ let _ your ba - la - lai - ka

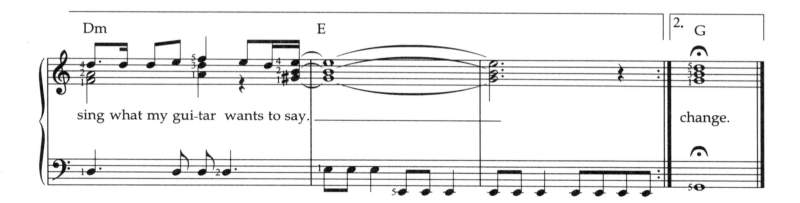

sing what my gui-tar wants to say. change.

Verse 2.

The world is closing in,
Did you ever think
That we could be so close, like brothers?
The future's in the air,
I can feel it everywhere,
Blowing with the wind of change.

Verse 3 (D.C.)

Walking down the street,
Distant memories
Are buried in the past forever.
I follow the Moskya
Down to Gorky Park
Listening to the wind of change.

YOU ARE NOT ALONE

Words & Music by Robert Kelly

way, I am here to stay, but you are not a - lone, but I am here with

you, though we're far a - part, you're al - ways in my heart, but you are not a -

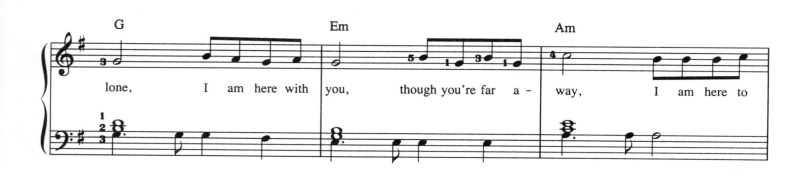

lone, I am here with you, though you're far a - way, I am here to

stay, but you are not a - lone, but I am here with you, though we're far a -

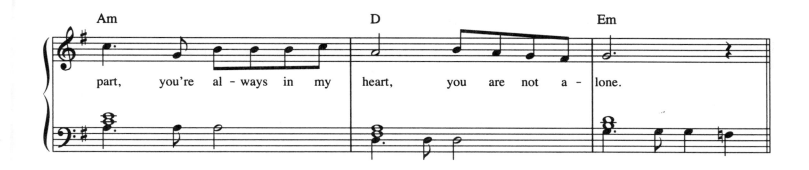

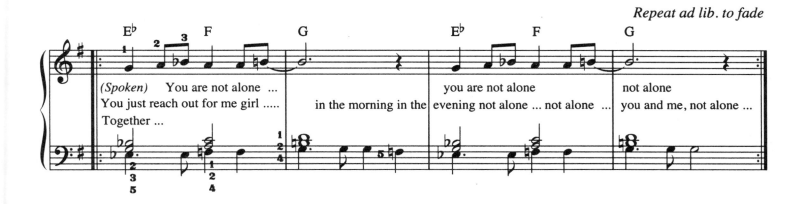

Verse 2:

You are not alone
I am here with you
Though you're far away
I am here to stay.
You are not alone
I am here with you
Though we're far apart
You're aways in my heart.
But you are not alone.

Verse 3:

Just the other night
I thought I heard you cry
Asking me to go
And hold you in my arms.
I can hear your breaths
Your burdens I will bear
But first I need you here
Then forever can begin.

Verse 4:

You are not alone
I am here with you
Though you're far away
I am here to stay.
But you are not alone
But I am here with you
Though we're far apart
You're always in my heart.
But you are not alone.

YOU GOTTA BE

Words & Melody by Des'ree
Music by Ashley Ingram

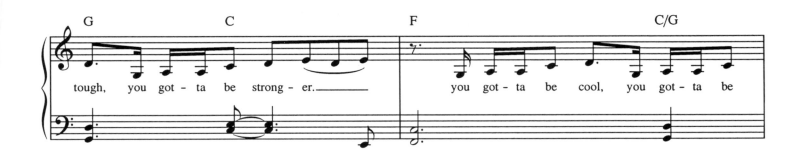

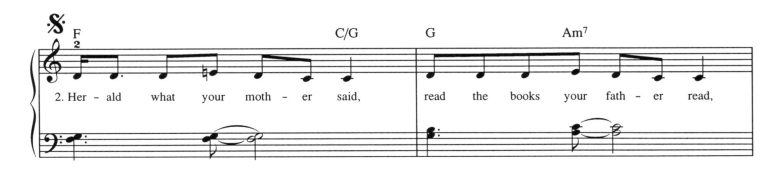

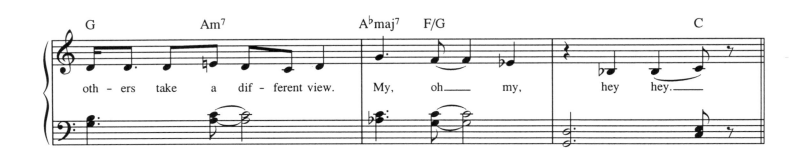

125

best part is dan-ger star-ing you in the face. Whoa.___ 3. Re-mem - ber

CODA

you got-ta be bad, you got-ta be bold, you got-ta be wis-er.___ You got-ta be hard, you got-ta be

tough, you got - ta be strong - er.___ you got-ta be cool, you got-ta be calm, you got-ta stay to-geth-er.___

All I know, all I know love will save_ the day.___ love will save_ the day.___

Verse 3:

Remember listen as your day unfolds
Challenge what the future holds
Try to keep your head up to the sky
Lovers they may cause you tears
Go ahead release your fears.
My, oh my, hey hey.

It's Easy To Play
The Series.

The 'It's Easy To Play' series offers you easy-to-read, simplified arrangements of music from the world's favourite performers and great composers.
Ideal for beginners, the music is newly engraved and includes chord symbols and lyrics where appropriate.

Abba AM22195	**Chopin** AM71747	**Familiar Songs** AM36419	**Nursery Rhymes** AM37706	**Rhythm & Blues** AM33549	**The Thirties** AM68313
Bach AM71721	**Christmas Songs** AM22641	**Folk** AM18987	**Oasis** AM936276	**Cliff Richard** AM90140	**The Forties** AM68321
Burt Bacharach AM937497	**Classical Themes** AM31659	**George Gershwin** AM68511	**Opera** AM32152	**Rock 'n' Roll** AM19555	**The Fifties** AM68339
Ballads AM63025	**Classics** AM19563	**Gilbert & Sullivan** AM24225	**Roy Orbison** AM77363	**Schubert** AM71762	**The Sixties** AM68347
Ballet Music AM32939	**Classics 2** AM60252	**Hymns** AM23698	**Party Time** AM90160	**Showtunes** AM26907	**The Seventies** AM68354
Beatles NO17907	**Richard Clayderman** AM61599	**Michael Jackson** AM77348	**Piano Duets** AM62514	**Paul Simon** PS10214	**The Eighties** AM68362
Beatles 2 NO90342	**Clayderman 2** AM65921	**Jazz** AM15280	**Pops** AM27228	**Paul Simon 2** PS10883	**TV Action Themes** AM62670
Bee Gees AM77355	**Phil Collins** AM65913	**Jazz 2** AM62258	**Pops 2** AM37904	**Soft Rock** AM74220	**TV Themes** AM63033
Beethoven AM71739	**Country 'n' Western** AM19530	**Elton John** AM61714	**Pops 3** AM65905	**Songs of England, Scotland & Ireland** AM31857	**TV Themes 2** AM89468
Blues AM15264	**Disney** WD10260	**Jerome Kern** AM80268	**Pops 4** AM67596	**Cat Stevens** AM24274	**Waltzes** AM20421
Blur AM936265	**Duran Duran** AM61755	**Latin** AM18995	**Pops 5** AM77132	**Strauss** AM83791	**West End Hits** AM90097
Bon Jovi AM936287	**Bob Dylan** AM78890	**Marches** AM24969	**Pops 6** AM91212	**Swing** AM20140	**Wet Wet Wet** AM935935
Boogie-Woogie AM23706	**Duke Ellington** AM65939	**Movie Music** AM953865	**Pops 7** AM936441	**Tchaikovsky** AM82926	**Stevie Wonder** AM40007
Carpenters AM23342	**Elvis** AM20868	**Mozart** AM71754	**Pub Songs** AM69279	**The Twenties** AM68305	**...and many more!**
Children's Songs AM29489		**Music Hall** AM69287	**Ragtime** AM14143		